CONTENTS:

C000240494

Foreword

Queen Mary's has had a long tradition of recording important events and anniversaries stretching back to its origin in 1929, when the Queen's Hospital was renamed Queen Mary's following its takeover by the London County Council. Although its official re-opening was the following year, it seems apt to celebrate its 75th anniversary now, not least because it coincides with the 30th anniversary of the current building, opened in 1974.

Previous anniversaries have been dignified in print. In 1929 an illustrated booklet described the facial injury work conducted from 1917 to 1925. In 1967, 50 years from the foundation of the Queen's Hospital, another booklet in similar style was produced. In 1984 Dr Bill Alexander described the activities of the first 10 years of the new Queen Mary's and in 1994 I wrote a history of the hospital, which is still in print.

This year, for the joint anniversary, it was agreed that we should compile a book of reminiscences and previously unseen photographs and Iris Presswell has worked tirelessly to produce it. I think that our offering reflects the caring and compassionate atmosphere of the hospital, with not a little humour and with a huge sense of team spirit. We are grateful to those who have contributed to it. Certainly it does us no harm to reflect on hospital life then, and now, and see what has changed – usually for the better.

Dr Andrew Bamji FRCP
Consultant Rheumatologist and Curator, Gillies Archives October 2004

Chairman Liz Butler and Finance Director Sheila Wilkinson cut the commemorative cake at the 75th anniversary service

Introduction

Queen Mary's has featured prominently in my life for more than ten years. As a non-executive director and, for the last 4 years, Chairman, I have experienced some of the most frightening, amusing, enjoyable and ultimately rewarding events of my life within its grounds.

Queen Mary's is not just the place where I work; it is my local hospital. It is where I have been treated, where my husband was repaired after he came off his motorbike and where one of my children receives on-going care. However, the ultimate testing of the service must have been when I had my youngest son at the hospital. A team of wonderful midwives and doctors supported me through pregnancy and delivery. Arriving in the small hours I knew I was in safe hands, from the moment the receptionist smiled in welcome until we were ushered out 16 hours later. Although my privacy was carefully protected it was overwhelmingly powerful to know that I was among friends. Now, whenever we drive past, Edward announces proudly that Queen Mary's is "his hospital".

The environment of Queen Mary's is very important to every one who visits or works here. But, building work is always costly and means a great deal of effort to find funding. Consequently the current redevelopment scheme worth £22m is cause for celebration. The work began with the building of the new day nursery for staff and to my great glee I was asked to "turn the first sod". I envisaged an elegant spade and a token hole; not so our builders, who supplied me with a hard hat and sat me in a digger. So, in a new silk jacket I was taught how to operate the machine and dug a rather deep hole. It was great fun and I now know what I want to do when I stop being a Chairman.

I am proud to have been associated with Queen Mary's Hospital and I hope that when you have finished reading this book, you will understand why.

Elizabeth Butler
Chairman, Queen Mary's Sidcup NHS Trust
(2000-2005)

Prelude

My first memories of Queen Mary's

I was born in 1906 in a house in Arbuthnot Road, New Cross, which is still standing to this day. (My daughter took me to see it earlier this year).

The First World War began in 1914 when I was 8, and it continued until I was 12, in 1918. At some time during those years, my Father took me to Sidcup by bus and tram on many Sunday mornings to take gifts of cigarettes to the injured servicemen who had returned from the trenches in France. They were being treated for their injuries, mostly to their eyes and faces, in the Nissen huts that were the first Queen Mary's Hospital, at the bottom of Frognal Avenue, Sidcup. (King George V and his Queen, Mary, was the reigning Monarch of that time.) The servicemen were often to be seen sitting along the roadside "seeing" the outside world, along what is today, the slip road from the A20 to Crittall's Corner, Footscray.

We felt we were doing something to repay them for the sacrifices they had made on behalf of the cause of freedom for our nation, Great Britain

Mrs Doris Marden
(aged 97)

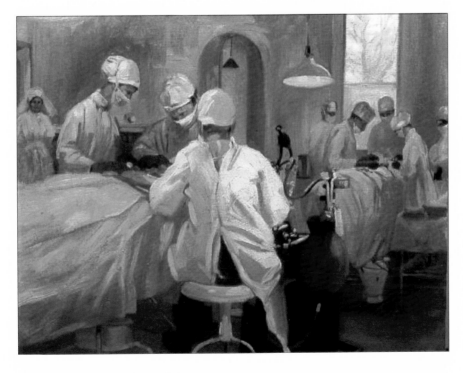

Walter Spradbery:
The Plastic Theatre
at the Queen's Hospital,
1918
(courtesy, Imperial War
Museum)

1929-1939

Princess Mary inspecting a guard of honour of Girl Guides when she opened Queen Mary's Hospital at Sidcup yesterday.

The official opening from the "Daily Sketch", Tuesday 22nd, 1930

Aerial view of the hospital in 1930. The new Sidcup by-pass is complete; note the lane, bottom right, that runs from the house's main entrance (now the entrance to Sunrise) straight onto the road! The white building, top right, is the old Crittall's factory, where B&Q now stands

Convalescence at Queen Mary's

In around 1928 my grandfather, James Charles Lambeth, a butcher by trade living in Islington, North London, was admitted to the old hospital because he had empyema [pus in the space round one lung –Ed]. The doctors in Islington had recommended he come here because the air was so clear and fresh, although I'm not sure this is so today, especially with the A20 so close by!

I didn't know that he had been an inpatient here until I started working at Queen Mary's and my grandmother mentioned it. She was pregnant at the time of her husband's admission and used to travel for hours with her three small children to visit him. This meant travelling on a succession of buses from one side of London to the other and because my young uncle was always travel sick they didn't stay on one bus for long and it made for a very long and disrupted journey, much to the disgust of his two older sisters! My grand mother loved the grounds, especially the rose garden and said how beautiful the area was. It was also a peaceful place to have their lunch after the terrible journey. Fortunately my grandfather recovered from his empyema and went home but sadly died in Islington in 1932 four years after his discharge.

When I first came to work at Queen Mary's in 1980 the hospital was much less busy than it is today and in those days it used to be possible to sit in the grounds of Frognal House. When things were not quite so hectic we secretaries used to take a picnic down into the grounds on a summer lunch-time. How times have changed, Queen Mary's is now a very big and busy hospital and Frognal House is a private nursing home. At least the Turkey Oak is still standing and son of Turkey Oak (planted by Frank Dobson) is growing tall outside the A&E and Outpatient entrance.

Valerie White, Medical Secretary

The "son of Turkey Oak", planted at the
official opening of the A&E extension, 1998
Left to Right:
Sir Edward Health, Lord Wallace,
John Austin MP, Nigel Beard MP,
Frank Dobson MP (Secretary of State for
Health), Clive Efford MP

DINING HALL, QUEEN MARY'S HOSPITAL, SIDCUP

Postcards of the hospital
just after the re-opening in
1930

The 1940's

Plasters, cinemas and knitting needles

During the 1940 Blitz on London I was in the London Fire brigade stationed in Surrey Docks and Deptford. I was injured during an evening raid when my right foot was crushed. I was to be taken to St Olave's Hospital, Rotherhithe, to which we were on route, but it had been bombed about half an hour earlier and bombs were still falling.

I spent about 3 months in Ward 21 at Queen Mary's – a modern ward for servicemen at the end of a wooden walkway, facing a field across which we were sometimes wheelchaired to the local cinema, much to the consternation of the second back row. Our open wounds were simply plastered and left to heal which was fine for us but the plasters became various shades of red, brown and green and stank to high heaven. We did not mind the colours of the plasters, but misbehaving patrons were inclined to move nearer the screen!

With over half the patients in such plasters it was our hobby to observe the faces of new visitors when they entered the ward of soldiers, firemen and airmen. Nursing staff were granted free passes through the pearly gates. From time to time my favourite nurse would borrow my knitting needle (used for freeing hairs caught up in the plaster) to fish out the maggots between my toes. These came from ordinary bluebottle flies through the windows. After a couple of 14 day plasters my wound had started to grow new skin all around the edge and it looked quite pink and healthy, although eventually I had 15 small pieces of skin grafted onto my foot. This, together with the amputation of a toe, was very successful and I was able to return to my unit.

A V-1 ("doodlebug") hits the hospital, 1944.

During the latter part of my stay I was appointed Honorary Chief Saline Solution Sprayer of chicken wire gauze frames over many wounded legs to keep the healing skin grafts moist. This was considered to be a promotion from my normal position of bedpan purveyor, having been fully instructed by the ward orderly "if they get too impatient tell them to do it in the bed and kick it out of the side".

The NHS is much improved today, though it is interesting that maggot treatment has been rediscovered!

Peter Clowe

This extraordinary snapshot was taken in 1944

The advent of the NHS in 1948, when the hospital was "rescued" from closure by the efforts of George Wallace MP, prompted the taking of a number of photographs, some of which appear on the following pages.

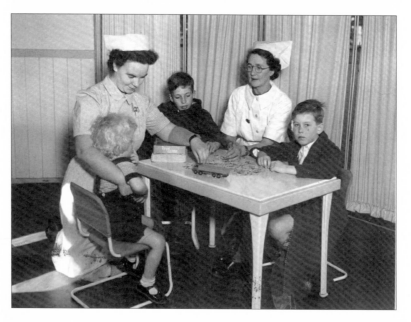

The children's ward, 1949

General view of the inside
of the "Horseshoe"

Spring 1949: admiring the
daffodils

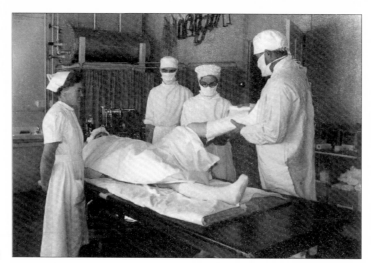

The Plaster Room

The Nursing School

The old Officers' Quarters

The 1950's

Many people remembered the Medical Superintendent, Clifford Ellingworth, with great affection. His dog used to sit outside Alan McCreary's office, so one day, having nothing better to do (those were the days) he sketched Rex. The accomplished drawing survives.

Nurses' Prizegiving, 1954.
Sheila Ogle is 5th from the right; the tall figure in the back row is **Clifford Ellingworth**

A ghost story

It was Christmas Eve.

I was on the Children's Ward (Ward 4) on night duty. There were two nurses for 16 beds. The day Staff Nurse was quite a character and did not always remember to write in the report all that was to be passed on to the next shift. This night we had a very sick 18-month-old boy baby about whom nothing had been written in the report. When I came on duty all was quiet, so I sat down to start my report at the big wooden table in the middle of the room. Somehow I felt it was going to be an easy night with no serious problems.

It was very dark. I shut the back door; we always had mice and hedge hogs outside and sometimes the hedgehogs came in. As the night went on the baby boy began to cry so I picked him up in my arms and cradled him, sang quietly to soothe him, but he felt very hot so I called Night Sister who immediately called the houseman, Roy Stewart. By the time he arrived the baby was hardly breathing. We began to give oxygen but it was not helping and within minutes Dr. Stewart told us the baby had died. It was my first encounter with infant death. In those days no parents stayed with their child; I felt so sad that the baby was all alone so I asked if I could go with the night porter to the Autopsy hut; by now it was raining. As we put the baby's body on the stretcher a bell began to ring. We all heard it very clearly. It was 3.30am. Q.M.H did not have a bell to ring and there was not a Church near enough. No one had ever heard a bell before and no one ever heard it again.

Sheila Anstall (née Ogle

14

Celebrity star

I nursed Joan Regan in 1956 at Queen Mary's Hospital after a road accident. She entertained everyone on the wards with her songs when convalescing; we were all invited to her show at the Palladium. I still treasure this photo with its inscription (I was a badminton player at the time): "To Rita, when I get rid of this plaster I'll take you up on a game of badminton. See you soon but not this way I hope. Love Joan Regan"

Rita Willis (née Whitney)

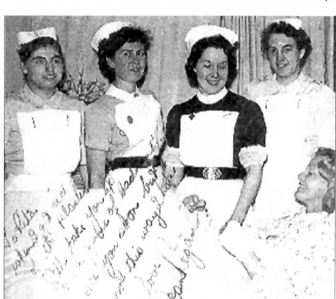

Celebrity star Joan Regan in 1956

International communication breakdown

When we first arrived at Q.M.H the war had not been over for too long and times were different. Nurses came from all over the world; one nurse was working with me on the Staff Ward and I was to help her all improve her English. Each morning we had the task of cleaning all the bedside lockers. On one particular morning I noticed she was not doing a very good job so I said to her "use some elbow grease!" After a few minutes I went into the supply room and she had everything off the shelves. I said "what are you looking for?" and she retorted "elbow grease". We both laughed after much explanation.

Sheila Anstall (née Ogle)

The Inter-hospital tennis doubles finalists; the Queen Mary's pair (on the right) were runners up to the Middlesex in the match played at St Charles' Hospital, West London

Anyone for tennis (or fruit salad)?

The hospital staff was small and we were like one family. All the staff got along very well. The nurses played tennis with the doctors and we were very competitive. Our salaries were very small; fortunately we had our food and housing and our laundry was done for us. We had very little to spend after being paid if we needed something expensive such as a tennis racquet. One month Madeline bought a new racquet because she was determined to beat the doctors at tennis. After going into town and buying it she had sixpence left to live on for a whole month! We had very few treats; butter and sugar were still in short supply. If we did have something special sent from home we all willingly shared. I remember being starved for fresh fruit and one day we had a big fruit salad given to us. Four of us sat on the floor of our room in Frognal House with this bowl of fruit and one spoon and shared it.

Madeline McLennan (née Wills)

Left:
Graduation day 1956.
Front row: (L to R)
Sheila Ogle, Ann Lewis.
Back row: Jean Bishop,
Madeline Wills,
Marian Walker.

Right:
Sheila Ogle weds
Dr Harold B. Anstall,
March 2nd 1957

The Christmas cakes,
1955

Food

I was appointed Catering Officer at Queen Mary's Hospital in 1949.
Like many hospitals in those days the catering was run by the Matron's
department and was delegated by her to a Sister's Housekeeper.

When I joined there was already talk about the building of a new
hospital as the present one was built in 1917 and was getting to the end
of its days. Nevertheless it was a very happy hospital for staff and patients.
There were two kitchens - one in the hospital for the patients, with a
dining room for non-resident staff, and another at Frognal House for
doctors and all nursing staff. Dr Ellingworth was the Medical
Superintendent when I went there, and always showed great interest in
the Catering Department. There were extensive hospital grounds; they
were always well kept and it was good on fine days to see patients
walking in them when possible.

In 1952 the hospital celebrated its 21st birthday and we had folk from
County Hall and others to tea in the large Recreation Hall
*[the difference in dates may reflect a delay in admitting patients after the
LCC takeover – or misplaced memory! - Ed]*

One of the special memories of Queen Mary's for me is of the many
interesting stories I heard about the Queen's Hospital days as we had 14
(I think) of the old facial cases working on the staff in varied positions.
It must have been a wonderful place for them because they were all so
badly wounded but they always spoke so well of those days –I feel I must
mention one person whose name I will never forget. He was a Colonel
Colvin who was the Administrative Officer who was obviously loved by
all these men as I gather with his great help they were healed
psychologically while Sir Harold Gillies and his team mended their
injuries.

During my time at Queen Mary's a "Get Together" was held as a doctor
from Australia who had been at the Queen's Hospital was visiting
England. Everyone who could be contacted - medical, nursing, patients
and ancillary staff- were invited from all over the British Isles. I only had
to arrange the tea. It was a lovely day and the tea was served outside
Frognal House. I can say that of the many special occasions I had to cater
for that was the best for me as it was absolutely marvellous to see
the wonderful spirit among them. It was one big Happy Family.
Mr Knight (the Supplies Officer) and I went to select the first electrically
heated trolleys the hospital had. These were a boon because the food
arrived piping hot on the wards.

L. Palmer (née Birchall – Catering Officer, 1949-1957)

Miss Birchall carving the
Christmas turkeys, 1955

The canteen staff at tea break

An addendum about food; Sheila Anstall recalls that there was a "Food Book" outside the canteen (and the doctors' dining room) in which criticisms could be entered. Harry Anstall recalls writing, in a fit of pique, a whole page about wet salads, and indicating to the catering staff that he was not a rabbit. Rationing was still in force when Sheila and Madeline arrived in 1953. Everyone had little jars with their names on for butter and sugar, but these would often be "raided". It sounds a bit like the shared fridges of today's students!

A hero's birthday

We had two night watchmen who had both been wounded very badly in WW1. They had gone through facial reconstructive procedures after the War but the price they paid for their Country was unbelievable. They were so disfigured, only night work was possible. They never looked us in the face, but we (the nurses) began to feel comfortable with them and would feed them a sandwich and a cup of tea on a cold night. Gradually we began to hear their stories. Stan the one I knew best told me he had never had a family, had never been to a dance, and had never enjoyed a girl friend even before the war. He had never had a Birthday Party or Christmas in a home environment. We never knew what his living conditions were in Sidcup but we imagined they were very sparse.

We were four privileged girls and decided he deserved better than this. We began plans to do something special for Stan. Eventually we found out when his birthday was and we began plans to surprise him. My mother, who was a Swiss trained pastry chef, made him a cake, decorated on top with his Military insignia, and we had masses of sandwiches, scones, sweet biscuits and other treats. It was so touching. We knitted him

19

scarves and mittens to fit over his badly burned hands; he had only two fingers left. It was such a wonderful experience for four young girls in the prime of life giving love and friendship to this man who gave so much of his life for us. This was Stan's last Birthday; he died very soon afterwards, with a memory that he had not been forgotten and as I reminisce writing this I remember him well, sitting munching on cake and sandwiches with four Nurses under a giant Turkey Oak Tree with garlands of camellia blossoms on the grass. These by the way, we were not supposed pick.

Sheila Anstall (née Ogle)

[Editor's note: We believe that Stan was Stan Cohen of the Tank Corps. We have his notes, but no indication of when and where he was wounded. Stan also ran a Sunday school class in Bromley and is remembered with great affection; John Clarke recalls that he would always send his charges a holiday postcard]

Tea under the Turkey Oak

Anything for a drink!

We were two nurses on night duty looking after 16 patients. One man was always teasing us and asking for a pint of beer. He had been sitting up in his chair when I suddenly realized after a while he was not there anymore; he was the only patient not put into bed. The male nurse with me went to look in the bathroom, but he was not to be found. The other patients told us he had gone to the pub! We called night sister who called the police. She was not too unhappy with us losing another patient as we had dealt with a death very early in the night. When the police came, we told them he was always asking for beer so they went to the local pub, the Barley Mow in those days, and sure enough he had walked there in his hospital gown, no shoes or socks and with drip hanging. The police men brought him back to the ward in a car, and he managed to bring back another pint. No harm was done... what is so unbelievable is that nobody saw him in all the distance he had to walk with his drip and called Q.M.H. and neither did the landlord.

Sheila Anstall (née Ogle)

A humourless Houseman

We worked long hours and always seemed to be in the middle of exams, so some days we became annoyed by sarcasm and mistreatment. At this period of time we had two housemen. One we all enjoyed working with and the other we tried to ignore and avoid because he was not too polite and gave us a hard time. When this one told us he was going to get married we saw our chance to get back at him as we realised he had no sense of humour and we had plenty. The laundry for both nurses and medical staff were all delivered to us at the back of the old kitchen in big brown boxes with our names boldly inscribed on them. We grabbed at the chance of confiscating his box. Four of us who were really angels in nurses' uniforms dragged his box into the nurses' home. We stayed up most of the night, stitching up all his belongings. We also thought as he was getting married it would be nice to have prettily embroidered pyjamas and handkerchiefs. We also decided they should all smell of very expensive perfume and they did by the time we were finished. The next morning before going on the wards we had to occupy the Sister who sat at the door while we put it back. As you can imagine this young house man was the only one who never came back and visited us again. We are still in touch with the other one after 50 years.

Madeline McLennan (née Wills)

A drunken houseman

Dr Geoff Daw [who, with Dr Golicz, made a film about nursing at Queen Mary's of which we have a copy – Ed] came in one night to the old Chicken Coop where the young doctors lived in those days. He was somewhat the worse for drink and as a result "lost" his room. Eventually he found his way in, as he thought, and started to get into bed. It was the wrong room, and the wife of the doctor whose room it was, who was abed and asleep began to scream. The other bleary eyed housemen got up to see what the noise was all about, put Geoff to bed and calmed her down. The next morning at breakfast she proclaimed "Dr. Daw, did you know you nearly got into bed with me last night?" whereupon he replied "My God, woman, I must have been drunk".

Harry Anstall (née Ogle)

Left
Beryl, Yorky and Eileen
Right
The Friends' Shop, 1959

Awakening from anasthesia

Dr. Ernie Matthews was an Orthopaedic Surgeon from Australia and had been a Bush Pilot. He was very flamboyant, quite short and with a mop of red hair. One night before going to a party he came to the ward to see his post-operative patients of the day. He was done out in full evening dress with a beautiful lady in evening gown (the works). As he stood by the bedsides asking each patient how they were, this one patient awakened for the first time, looked at them and exclaimed "My God! I am in Heaven!" Matthews replied "I hope you bloody well aren't!"

Sheila Anstall (née Ogle)

The 1960's

A Houseman's tale

I qualified at UCH in Nov. 1960, saw an advert in the BMJ, applied, was appointed an HS and started work at Queen Mary's on the 1st. Dec 1960, the first non-Guys man to darken their doors!

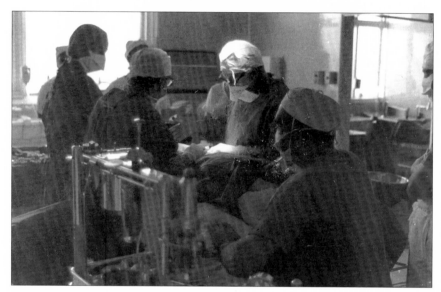

"Nobby" Clark operating; "Fitz" Fitzpatrick giving the anaesthetic

In those days, you covered ENT, Eyes, Dentistry, some Orthopaedics all the time and Casualty in the evenings and overnight! Thus I have removed tonsils, corrected squints, wired-up broken jaws as well as appendicectomies, hernias, varicose veins etc., etc. Most of this unsupervised after the first two weeks! If 'Nobby' Clark sent in an appendix from a DV, you did as you were told and took it out. My first 'appendix' was a ruptured ovarian cyst so I learned some Gynae pretty rapidly through a keyhole incision. 'Nobby' merely said I should have taken the appendix as well!

After 6 months, I was appointed as House Physician under Tony Reeves and after a few weeks, John Williams was appointed as the second Consultant Physician. I don't think he ever recovered from the shock of having a free-wheeling houseman who did his own thing. One night, looking after a lad of 12-13 with nephrotic syndrome (kidney disorder), I grew tired of watching him becoming more and more oedematous and not responding to Mersalyl or some new diuretic that John was trying out so I transfused him carefully with hyper tonic Dextran, sat with him overnight, and by the morning he was no longer oedematous. John got rather excited on his ward round the following morning until he found out what had been done overnight. Although I had ruined his trial of what was later marketed as 'Diamox', as the lad never looked back after my escapade, I survived with the firm advice, 'don't do it again'. Another aspect of this job was that I looked after the chest cases for Paul Forgacs, so I too have tapped many a chest although not at 30,000 feet. I also looked after the Geriatrics whose preferred management for faecal incontinence was Kaolin et Morph or Cretae c Opio, 5 days a week, and a violent soap enema on the other 2. Brandy was the preferred night sedative; pheno barbitone sent them 'do-lally'.

Nights on Casualty were quite exciting at times. In 1960-61 the stretch of road from Mottingham to the Dutch House Public House was known as the "Mad Mile' and the lads on their powerful motor bikes with a leather-clad dolly bird on the back used to try and hit the 'magic ton' i.e. 100 mph. The problem was that the bend through the railway arch at that time was much more acute than now and if they didn't make the bend; they went through the railings of the pub car park and on more than one occasion were literally 'chipped' which meant the houseman on-call had to re-assemble the pieces before identification by the police and relatives. Those that survived had their multiple grazes treated with various coloured lotions, acroflavin, brilliant green, iodine, lotio rubra etc. so they left the department looking more like Red Indians than ferocious "Hells Angels". It was most important to keep a very straight face and professional manner whilst giving instructions to the nurses as to which colour went on which bit of damaged skin. Surprisingly perhaps, they often came back to express their thanks. Of course, one also set the standard fractures and gave the general anaesthetic as well.

George Lee's attempt at open-heart surgery happened during my time *[open chest resuscitation was performed; it made the national papers, but sadly the patient succumbed – Ed]* and more than one keen houseman started to carry a scalpel in their top pocket just in case! (not me).

The "Daily Mail" reports the penknife surgery

Among the other personalities I remember, Freddy Herman was unforgettable. He had a tongue hardened with aqua regia and woe-betide any houseman that crossed his path. The most heinous crime was for a new House Officer to take 'his' place at the Mess table, followed closely by using the oil and vinegar that he used to make his own 'special' brew of salad dressing. His sarcasm when a simple House Officer used the wrong description of some chunk of pathology or asked for what in his view was an inappropriate investigation was born of literary genius at times.

He had another side, when a man was admitted with 90% burns having fallen into a vat of boiling varnish at a local printing ink factory, it was Freddy that called on his experience gained during the war and "held my hand' as we worked out his IV fluid requirements, whilst we waited 3 days for Guys to take him on for dialysis. The patient left Queen Mary's in good condition but he did not survive his renal failure.

He also spotted Malaria from a temp chart that all had missed and took great delight in teasing his consultant colleagues. It was he however that looked at the blood film 'out of hours' at the next spike of temperature. Glyn Jones, the Radiologist, was another Freddy Herman in many senses, having an acid tongue and was somewhat confusing to work with as the 'goal posts' were apt to move almost on a daily basis as regards what X-ray request he would or would not accept.

Basil Sanderson, the Gynaecologist, was rugby-mad and would transfer the venue of his ward round to Twickenham if there were a good match.

Mr. Percival, the other surgeon, used to have his dog with him at all times except in theatre and it was the House Surgeon's job to hold his very bad-tempered Doberman outside the ward whilst he did the ward round inside. One day he was quite late for his round and he explained that he had had to sew a lad's nose back on as this lad had very un-wisely poked his nose into his car with the dog inside. He liked to do plastic surgery as he had worked with McIndoe [at the Queen Victoria Hospital, East Grinstead - Ed] as his registrar so I learnt a bit about that subject as well although it paid to keep quiet about David Matthews whose firm I was on at UCH.

Accommodation for the juniors was a low hut to the right of Frognal nicknamed the 'chicken run' – paper-thin walls, no heating, communal bathroom and no married quarters. Not that these conditions deterred one South African House Surgeon who had supercharged hormones and was determined to work his way through the nurses home. The nights could be very noisy! No intrusive bleeps in those days. There was a system of light boxes hanging from the ceilings with numbers 1 to 4, which could be 'still', or 'flashing'. I remember my call-code was 2 still combined with 3 flashing. After a time one developed a sixth sense as to when your lights were flashing and response times were short.

Brian Camp (retired GP, Erith)

Full circle

I am loath to admit it, but at the age of almost 16, I began work in the Cashier's Office in the old Queen Mary's, which was at the front of the hospital, not far from Casualty. From here we could see the ambulances coming in, sometimes delivering the broken and bleeding results of road accidents. I worked there for about a year and a half.

The hospital then consisted of huts of course, with covered, but open, corridors connecting them. The main wards were laid out in the shape of a horseshoe, with the main entrance at the 'heel' of the shoe. From the Cashier's office one looked out onto ward 1A and part of the grounds of Frognal House, with the large ancient oak tree, which was a lovely view for us. The office connecting with ours was that of the Hospital Secretary, then Mr Parker, with other offices connecting to his office also, which his secretary occupied, amongst others.

My duties included helping to make up the weekly wages in cash, which was brought in each week by the hospital van without a security guard. We then paid out each member of staff, obtaining signatures for the wage packets, and once a month we also distributed the monthly pay cheques in the same way. This meant that at some time, all of the hospital employees came into our office, from Consultants down to the cleaners. I met them all. One of the consultants I remember very well was Dr Reeves, after whom Reeves ward was later named. He was such a lovely man, quite unpretentious, at a time when many consultants would not even acknowledge us lesser mortals.

I also had responsibility for making copies of the hospital minutes and other confidential papers on the Gestetner Copier. Because this involved the use of ink, in order to protect my clothing, I was provided with a white coat, which was all that was available. I remember feeling quite important as I made my way round the hospital delivering the copied items, but in due course there was a complaint from the doctors, who said that I looked like one of them, since they all wore long white coats back then. My boss never quite found an answer to this dilemma!

At that time there were a great many young porters employed to push patients around, either in wheelchairs or beds, from place to place. This was rather nice for a girl of 16! Since another of my duties was to restore personal belongings to persons who had come in via Casualty, who were for the most part young men who had come to grief on their motor bikes (often on Death Hill) this was rather nice too! They often set up quite a hullabaloo on the ward! The downside of this duty was that we often had to go through the belongings of the deceased with the relatives, in an open office, with people coming and going. I always felt for them. It was quite unsuitable really, at such a dreadful time for them.

I remember too, what a long walk it was down to Path Lab back then. Ward 10 was also down there in the 'back of beyond'. On the way one could see the very many feral hospital cats, who lived underneath the wards. A lot of people would feed them, patients and staff alike. Interestingly, one of the young men who worked in the Path Lab at that time, later went on to do medical training after I had left the hospital, and years later I found him at my front door. I had called the doctor out to my young son, and he turned out to be the GP on duty! He had his own family by then, and he was to serve as my GP for years to come.

Another very interesting trek for me was from our office up to Finance, which was then based upstairs in Frognal House. I did this walk in all weathers, taking or picking up various things, but I loved it. It took me through the grounds, which had once been planted as an exotic garden. There still remained many of the original Rhododendrons, some beautiful varieties, one of which was crimson, and bloomed in the snow as I remember. An amazing sight. But by far my favourite thing in the grounds was the old oak. In the summer children off the ward would have picnics under its very heavy boughs in the shade, nurses spreading blankets on the ground. The boughs hung low and had been propped up to help support their weight. It spread out in a huge circle, giving a large area of shade. It appeared on all the hospital stationery, as a symbol of Queen Mary's Hospital.

Whilst I worked there, the 'new' hospital was in the planning stage, with the accommodation blocks currently being built. In the summer a swimming pool was provided for the staff [to the east, just beyond the large staff car park we have today - Ed]. It was a temporary structure, but we had a great deal of fun using it. The main block was constructed later, by which time I was working as a dental nurse elsewhere.

It is strange that I now find myself at the upper end of my working life, once more working in Queen Mary's Hospital, and so close to A&E. I would be very interested to make contact with anyone who either remembers me from those times, or worked in the hospital in 1963/64. I should also love to be able to walk in the grounds of Frognal House again, and to see the Old Oak.

Hazel Roffey, Secretary, Social Work Department

Lady Gillies at the hospital's Golden Jubilee, 1967, with many of Sir Harold's Great War patients

Those were the days!

Ever since I can remember, I have always wanted to be a nurse, and when my family of five was complete, I was accepted as an auxiliary nurse at Queen Mary's Hospital. The hospital as we know it wasn't there, but in its grounds, in a very rural setting, was the old Queen Mary's, known as "the huts." These were white weatherboard buildings, with duckboards that joined the wards together. The huts were erected in the First World War for facially disfigured servicemen, and in the hospital archives there are many photographs of nursing staff and surgeons who attended these brave men. Theatre comprised a hut that opened out onto a duckboard, and when a patient had undergone an operation, he was wheeled out into all the elements, to his respective ward, seemingly no ill effect! Cats were abundant. All types! There were one-eyed, three-legged, devoid of ears, all malformed, throw-outs of nature. They "nested" under the stilts of the huts and were completely wild. The "cat catchers" would descend every so often and 'dispose of these poor creatures, but after a short while, other cats would appear and take over from their parents, and multiply in great profusion! Then there were the birds. These nested wherever there was a place to lay their eggs. As we walked along the duckboards we could see little beaks peeping from their precarious nests and anxious mothers fly ing past our heads, with their tasty morsels for their babes. That was truly wonderful. We were at one with nature.

Not only cats and birds, but horses as well! Gypsy families were in the adjacent fields, and they had many horses. Sometimes they would saunter over to the huts and pop their heads in the ever open window and look to the patients and nurses for a tasty tit-bit. Often it would be peppermints, as the patients seemed to have and endless supply of them. I think it must have been therapeutic, as it was the outside world and nature coming in, in a very gentle way.

The wards were spotless, and they were known by numbers. The matron was Miss Allcock, very efficient and visited the wards very regularly. Her deputy was Mr Linale, a very kindly man. There was no M.R.S.A and very little infection given the nature of the hospital facilities, amazing!

The nurses' Christmas pantomime, 1968

The uniforms were blue striped dresses with white aprons. No jewellery, make-up and hair was tied back or in a bun with our hats were firmly secured on our head. We were all very proud of our uniforms and very proud to be nurses. It was very cosmopolitan, black and white, Chinese, Mauritian and many lovely Irish nurses, we all worked as one. My first ward was the orthopaedic ward, a long room that seemed to go on forever. In the evening we did a complete "back-round" where we washed and massaged every back and bottom to ensure no pressure areas. All flowers were removed and replaced in the morning. There was a bed pan round also so that each patient was made comfortable for the night. Horlicks and night-time drinks were given out, lights were dimmed and all would be peaceful.

The sister on that ward was Mrs. McFeely, who later became a nursing officer. We were in awe of her. We could hear the clip-clop of her shoes approaching and we would be aware of the strict regime that we all were part of and it ensured that our ward was run efficiently and securely. It was a very busy ward and a 'heavy' one, lots of lifting and bed changing. Open-ended pillow cases faced the windows and sitting on a bed was unthinkable, whether you were a nurse or whether you were a visitor! No Christian names were exchanged between patient and nurse, and there was a feeling of deep respect all round.

Time to travel on. Mr Linale asked me to leave orthopaedics and move on to ward 9, the private ward. This ward comprised of several separate rooms to accommodate each paying patient. The sister on this ward was Sister Chatton, a lovely lady who was totally dedicated to her vocation. If the food sent up to the patients was not up to sister's satisfaction, she would open up her 'larder' and produce tins of soup or eggs, and we would serve a meal to her standards. The soup would be served in a dainty bowl, the bread would have the crusts removed, a dainty tray would appear with a doily and the eggs poached or scrambled. We would all take part in this culinary procedure. Always, tea or coffee would be given in pretty cups, with biscuits to boot. It was a very happy ward, we all learnt such a lot as the diagnosis and prognosis would be so varied for each patient as they joined our happy throng.

I remember one patient who will be nameless, admitted to the ward with a myocardial infarction, and he was on bed-rest. Carrying out normal duties I entered his room and found him fully dressed grinning from ear to ear and holding several packets of peppermints in his hands. "I have a confession to make" said he, "I have just been to the shops and placed a bet and bought these for the horses, I managed to 'phone for a taxi and was there and back in no time!" Can you imagine the furore that emerged? His bottle of whisky that we discovered under his bed was locked away and his clothes removed until further notice. He seemed none the worse for wear and thank goodness no-one was held responsible for 'the great escape.'

There was a cottage hospital in Sidcup near Birkbeck road [the Barnard Medical Centre stands on the site – Ed]. When this little hospital was short staffed they 'borrowed' nurses from Queen Mary's I was often asked to go there and it was like stepping back in time. There were two nursing sisters who were in charge, one being Sister O'Malley, a lovely Irish lady, who enjoyed a little wager on the horses. When it was our break time we were allowed in the dining room where we sat whilst sister poured tea or coffee from a silver pot. We drank from pretty china cups and we were given homemade cakes! It was like dining with royalty! During the partaking of refreshments, sister would be studying form and picking the winners from the newspaper. The two sisters always ensured that their half starved protégées were looked after and fed properly. We always had a cooked meal. I remember nursing there with such happiness.

Total devotion and loving care was given to all by all the nursing staff. It was a haven of love.

45819. Sidcup Cottage Hospital. F.F.&Co

The Morgue

The morgue was situated in the grounds of the hospital and when there was a death at night, sister and I would wheel the body through the hospital and out into the morgue. It was so dark and eerie and I was always nervous. One particular sister would often uncover a body that was already there and say "I'm just making sure he/she is all right" and then she would replace the sheet...

June Nelson

Training for real nursing

9th August 1963 was my 18th birthday, the day I had been looking forward to since starting my pre-nursing course two years previously. The next day with bags packed I left home to start my general nurse training. I had chosen Queen Mary's because… well to be honest I'm not sure why! I'd been accepted by St Bartholomew's and The Royal Free Hospital in London but there was something about Matron Redding that made my mind up to train here. Arriving at the nurses' home was something of a culture shock, a large wooden shack, a large Home Sister who stood no nonsense, late passes were very limited, but of course we young students found ways of entering the home late at night when we supposed to be tucked up in our beds. The laundry chute was a favourite until we got caught. Meals were taken in the dining room. These were freshly cooked and delicious, especially breakfast. The rooms in the nurses home were single, double or triple all very basic but they did have a washbasin. Needless to say visitors were very restricted and never men in your rooms. Believe it or not there was chicken wire up at the windows to stop prowlers. By the time I had completed my training new homes had been built, absolute luxury. Most of these have now been demolished and Hyde Housing is in their place.

The new residences in 2004, (built 1996)

My first ward before entering PTS was ward 18 Women's Geriatric (elderly care nowadays). This was the ward to learn real basic care and how not to lose or mix-up false teeth!!! The ladies were a real eye-opener, particularly Granny Gurr; my goodness, did we learn a lot from her. She was a real lady one minute and the next swearing like a trooper. As with all the wards there was a veranda so that the patients could be wheeled out to enjoy the fresh air. All the wards were built on brick stilts and under all the wards lived an array of animals including the feral cats to be enticed with tit-bits. I left ward 18 to enter PTS in the October and after learning so many skills including how to give an injection into an orange, we were let loose onto the wards all feeling very proud of our crisp white aprons and hats. My first ward as a student nurse was ward 17 (men's medical). Mr Williams was the charge nurse who taught us so much. Team nursing had not been invented but after report each morning we would divide into two sets and we would race to finish "our" side, the work including bed baths, stripping and remaking the beds, making sure that the hospital corners were pristine before inspection by Mr Williams, then by Matron or Deputy-Matron. Oh yes, each day there was a round by Matron.

Dinner on the ward 18, 1949

All the wards were the same layout (except the private ward); a long Nightingale design with swing-doors which opened onto the circle or duckboards, I cannot ever remember them being locked. Numerous windows ran the length of the ward and there was a day room either halfway down or at the end of each ward. Most wards had a kitchen, a sister's office, the sluice and bedpan washer, bathroom, toilets and a sterilizing room. This was where we cleaned, sharpened needles, where all the metal kidney dishes and bowls were polished until they shone and where we cleaned the glass syringes as well before putting them in the sterilizer. We also had to make our own cotton wool balls. No CSSD (Central Sterile Supplies Department) in those days!

Throughout my training amidst the sheer slog at work, learning new skills, attending lectures (when you would prefer to be in bed after night duty) there was a social life. This included digging out and making a swimming pool. The staff would put on a show each Christmas. One performance that stands out in my memory was a take of the Rolling Stones song Little Red Rooster; another was certain male members of staff performing Swan Lake in tutus and big boots.

Completion of my nurse training saw me wearing the coveted navy belt with a beautiful silver buckle that my father gave me. After a period of being a staff nurse I left Queen Mary's to undertake further and post-graduate training. After working in other hospitals I returned to Queen Mary's as sister of ward 4 children's surgery. I restructured the ward and introduced open visiting, play for all the children, no more sitting in beds – not moving in case they creased the sheets. Mr Clark and Mr Percival had to watch where they were walking on their rounds as little ones zoomed up and down on their push-along trikes.

Queen Mary's has certainly seen a lot of change but would I swap my training in those old wooded huts? No never!

Yvonne Dyer

Yvonne Dyer with colleagues in Frognal House

Taking a dip in the hospital's swimming pool

The medical secretary's
office at Queen Mary's,
c.1960

Erith Hospital is, of
course, now part of the
Queen Mary's group, but
was originally in the
Woolwich Hospital group.
This photo was taken in
1963, at the time of the
opening of the new
Outpatients' department

The 1970's

Pat Howley displays one of her watercolours of the rebuilding; these were on display for many years in the Front Hall, until they were stolen

A dog's life

Many may remember Dr Maria Sokolowska who ran the X-ray department more or less single-handed in the late 1970s. She could be very helpful, but always reported films in complete darkness and one took one's life in one's hands visiting her office – for beneath her desk sat her little dog. Sometimes it was not quite beneath the desk… then, in the Stygian gloom, one trod on it, and it would bite. The tale that the dog did the reporting is apocryphal.

Farewell to the old

I joined the portering staff during the final few months' life of the hutted buildings in November 1973.

It soon became apparent to me that besides the staff and patients, we had other residents on side, namely wild cats, crickets and an army of Pharaoh ants, the latter being introduced into Sidcup via the soldiers arriving from the Middle East during World War 1. These creatures were very much at home among the warmth and humidity of the under floor steam pipes and every so often one of the unfortunate cats would become trapped between the pipes and slowly casserole itself, creating a very nasty smell which would permeate up through the floor and was known to last for up to a week. On one occasion one died directly under the switchboard floor and how bravely Pam and Barbara, the telephonists, stayed at their posts has not been documented until now.

We had one cardiac arrest "crash" trolley in the whole hospital; which was situated in A&E. It consisted of an old, second-hand children's "Pedigree" pram complete with buckled wheel. This said wheel created a tendency to swerve around violently when travelling at speed. The trick was to try and keep the pram under control with one hand and use the other to try and hold everything down and prevent things from falling off!

Then and now;
B Block from the east,
1973 and 2004

We finally started the move into our new hospital in 1974, (making very sure those Pharaoh ants did not follow us) overseen by the tireless efforts of the Hospital Secretary Mr Ron Thompson. It may have been old, it may have been worn out, but I know that staff and patients will remember the "old" hospital with a lot of affection. Queen Mary's has a very special and unique history.

Ian Ray – Facilities Department

New hospital, old fashioned bedrest...

Life went on in the huts, this very rural and old fashioned hospital.
Patients who were post-operative and recuperating had their beds
wheeled out onto the verandas so they could be in the fresh air and
enjoy the peace and quiet of the countryside. Soon it was to change.
There were rumours that a new hospital was to be erected in the grounds
and the huts were to go. Meetings were held to discuss this new project,
and the nursing staff were asked to discuss the naming of the new wards.
What did we think of naming the wards after places in Kent? What about
Chislehurst for the gynae ward, Whiteoak for paediatrics [after the old
paediatric hospital in Swanley], Foxbury for surgical. Then there were
Danson [*what happened to that, I wonder? – Ed*] and Ruxley, Bickley,
Lamorbey, and Gillies in memory of a consultant who was there many
years before.

Who are they all?
Representatives of all staff
groups at the hospital's
opening, 1974

With great reluctance we left our huts and entered the great unknown.
We said goodbye to Frognal House, where the school of nursing was and
where we had our meals. This was a listed building and had great
presence. My allocated ward in the 'new hospital' was Chislehurst, the
gynaecological ward. I was very happy in my new domain. Everywhere
was spick and span. There were twenty-nine beds to a ward, six beds to a
bay and side rooms which were either for private patients or for sick or

isolation patients. On that ward we encountered sorrow, when a mother-to-be lost her babe, or when cancer struck, young girls having abortions, sometimes there would be a comic on her locker and a much loved teddy in her bed. Hysterectomies were hospitalised for two weeks, as were repairs. These patients were promoted to bay four after a few days whist they recovered and were quite self-sufficient. They were loath to leave the safe haven, as they likened it to a convalescent home. They made firm friendships with their contemporaries and the nursing staff. Some patients were on complete bed-rest for the whole of their pregnancy as they had suffered miscarriages previously.
We all became very close.

June Nelson

Return of the wanderer

It was at this time after getting married, I found out that I was pregnant and the foundations for the red brick building (as we called B block) were being laid. Returning to work I found myself working in a totally new environment, very modern and a hint of luxury. No steam sterilizers!! I worked on Whiteoak for a while before leaving Sidcup to move into deeper Kent. I couldn't drive at the time so once more left Queen Mary's.

The lure of Queen Mary's happened again and I returned in 1995 to work on the Neonatal Unit.

Oh yes, before I forgot, the famous Grey Lady of Queen Mary's, did she exist? Oh yes. I saw her. But that is another story.

Yvonne Dyer

1974: Coco the clown visits maternity

The 1980s

Team Briefing

A bit of fun is perhaps permissible and in the late 80's, when all again was doom and despair money-wise I decided to lighten things up a bit with an April Fool. "Team Briefing" had just been invented; this was aimed at improving workforce communication, morale and team spirit.

I drafted a letter, dated April 1st and sent it out over the signature of the Hospital Administrator, John Stevenson, to all consultants and senior members of staff. In it I suggested that Japanese industry had found it helpful as a team building exercise to sing a company song at the start of the working day, thought that this was an excellent idea to adopt and attached two songs (with dreadfully trite words, which will surprise no-one who has heard my poems for retiring staff members) with a request to return the tear-off slip at the bottom, indicating which song was the better.

I circulated the document in re-usable envelopes to disguise their origin, and awaited results.

16 replies were received.

My erstwhile physician colleague, Bill Alexander, had another "take" on Team Briefing. He broke into the Administrator's office one evening and left a pair of underpants on the desk, labelled "Team Briefs".

Andrew Bamji

Booklet compiled by
Dr Bill Alexander
for the
10th anniversary
of the
new hospital

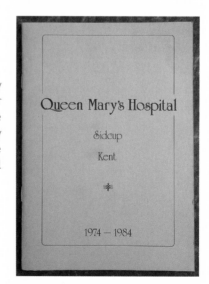

Queen Mary's Hospital

Sidcup

Kent

1974 — 1984

The Gardener-Surgeons

Two surgeons, **Jeremy Wilson** and Peter Savage, were appointed to the new Queen Mary's in 1974; it seems strange to think that for ten years they were the only two, being joined by John Payne in 1985. Mr Wilson was very much a Queen Mary's man and fastidious about the appearance of the hospital. It was he who was the driving force behind the establishment of the Arts and Environment Committee, and for many years chose the paintings supplied by the charity "Paintings in Hospitals" and scattered strategically in corridors and stairwells. The charity bought young or unfashionable artists' work, and if it developed any value it would be sold on to finance future acquisitions; one of the most expensive paintings at Sidcup was by Ivon Hitchens, while another by Ruskin Spear was in the old ophthalmic outpatients. Visiting the yearly exhibition to choose new stock was great fun, as one acquired nice things without spending any money.

But the outside of the hospital was just as important. The shrubbery in front of 'B' Block got out of hand (largely because the grounds staff were laid off because of cutbacks). The then Administrator was not sympathetic, claiming there were other priorities. Jeremy took action, bringing in a number of colleagues and their families over a weekend to regain control– but found that there was nowhere to dispose of the vast pile of prunings.

When the administrator returned to his office on the Monday (then, as now, at the right hand corner) he discovered he could not see out. The clippings had been heaped all around his windows, and on his desk was a neat card which read "Savage, Wilson and Payne. Gardening Contractors. Estimates free. No job too small".

Opening of the
Postgraduate Centre,
1986; left to right,
Jeremy Wilson,
Brian Hord (Health
Authority Chairman),
Edward Heath,
Mike Lancaster Smith

The 1990s

The case of the Houseman's bed

In days of old (like the 1990s) there was a Doctors' Mess and suitably placed on-call rooms for the duty junior staff, later moved, under pressure of space, to a ward side-room. Rotas meant that these were "hot-bedded" and it was not unknown for juniors to arrive, dog-tired and ready for sleep, to find that the bed linen had not been changed for some days.

One decided after two disgusting beds on successive on-calls that enough was enough. He wheeled the bed out of the room, into a lift and down the Admin corridor, parking it with some difficulty in the Hospital Administrator's office with a note asking if he would sleep in a bed like this.

By all accounts there was an explosion when he arrived the next morning. Things improved – for a while!

Andrew Bamji

The first Trust Board, 1993. Left to right: standing – Dr John Kensit (Medical Director), Valerie Tandy, Michael Hollingsworth, Cheryl Miles (Chief Nurse), Mike Sillitoe (Personnel Director), Lady Ann Jenkins, Gary Belfield (Service Development Manager), John Walters seated – Stephen Collinson (Chief Executive), Colin Campbell (Chairman), David Blake

Police, camera, action!

Occasionally the hospital becomes a crime scene. I got a call from the Deputy Commissioner of the Metropolitan Police; it appeared that we had the mother of someone under the witness protection scheme in the hospital and they wanted to arrange a visiting time. The bad news was that about ten armed officers arrived, having had a tip off that there was going to be an attack on this witness. We, of course, could tell no one. After checking the story Stephen Collinson [the hospital's Chief Executive] and I disappeared down the basement street but they wanted exclusive use of the lift for an exit route, so Stephen stayed in the basement lift bay to hold the lift button & stop people using the lift. He was not exactly popular! When we got to the third floor all hell broke loose when the police spotted a known criminal associate – guns were drawn and myself and the witness, who looked like he had fallen out of "The Godfather" were rushed out through the ward into the rear car park. Vehicles sped into the distance and I returned to my office with the story – completely forgetting about poor Stephen, who was still patiently holding the lift button in the basement!

Then there was the Woolwich building society armed robbery. The robber (whose wife happened to be a patient in maternity) had parked his car outside the Sidcup branch but it stalled and he ran for it with the cash and shotgun into the maternity department of the hospital pursued by several policemen. They stopped at the door and called for reinforcements and within a few minutes two bus loads of armed policemen and a helicopter were on the scene. The inspector in charge advised us it was a low profile operation, which seemed slightly surreal, as he had to shout over the drone of the helicopter and the police loud hailer demanding the man surrender as the hospital was surrounded by armed police. In the evacuation of the unit a visitor dropped his ski mask and was arrested. His wife was in her bed, with his shotgun tucked beside her under the bed clothes…

Colin Campbell
(Chairman 1992-2000) addresses the attendees at the farewell party for Stephen Collinson (Chief Executive), 2000

43

A nice little earner

Many people do not know that the hospital still owns the large field down Watery Lane. One day Stephen Collinson & I were walking the estate with Gary Belfield [Service Development Manager, later Director of Operations – Ed] and came across some gypsies feeding their horses. I suggested they clear off, as they were on hospital property, and that they take their horses with them. They indignantly replied that they had been paying 'rent' (in cash) for several years to someone who called round weekly! Yes, it was a nice little earner for one of our staff… no doubt it helped their early retirement fund!

Colin Campbell, Chairman (1993-2000)

Fire, fire!

Apart from his bold beard and shock of orange hair, **Bill Alexander** (consultant in diabetes and endocrinology and inveterate pipe-smoker) was never happy with the hospital's no smoking policy. Those who know his retirement portrait cannot but admire the snook thereby cocked. When the Diabetic Unit, then housed in E Block, was fitted with a smoke alarm as part of the fire protection upgrade, it was not of much use, as after a false alarm or two he wrapped it in a plastic bag.

Andrew Bamji

Bill Alexander's retirement, 1999: left to right Sue Ward, Brian Gould, WDA, Kevin Kelleher, Richard Geraghty, Mike Lancaster Smith, Michael Gotlieb, Stephen Collinson, Charles Shee

It wasn't a real bomb, Sir...

Disaster planning was a particular specialty of surgeon and Medical
Director Peter Savage, who had an international reputation in the subject
and set up the Queen Mary's system. This required occasional testing,
and one Sunday an exercise was run to simulate a terrorist attack on a
hotel in Erith (hardly a likely scenario, but it enabled the enlistment of a
rescue helicopter based at Manston to ferry "casualties" who were landed
on the golf course).

Not everything went to plan. No-one thought to phone the switchboard
to let them know the helicopter was on its way, so several volunteer
casualties nearly froze while waiting to be stretchered into the hospital.

However worse was to come. Peter decided that security had to be tested,
and sent a message to switchboard that word had been received that there
was a bomb in the hospital. However he omitted to say it was part of the
exercise. Switchboard promptly and properly followed the correct
procedure to the letter and within a short while the Bomb Squad arrived.

The report of the exercise does not, in my recollection, include the severe
dressing-down of the Disaster Co-ordinator from a very angry senior
police officer whose armed squad had been sent on a wild goose chase.

I can recall that the Disaster Plan was once activated for real – when a
train came off the arches in Bexley village. Four minor casualties were
received, reminiscent of the newspaper headline "Small earthquake.
Not many dead".

Andrew Bamji

H.R.H.
Princess Michael of Kent
with Selim Morcos
(Consultant Gynaecologist)
at the official opening of
the Kent Women's Wing,
1995

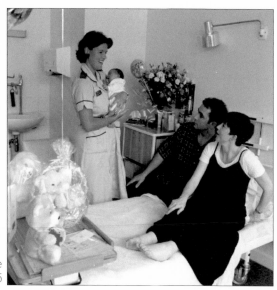

Midwife Marsh with the
Weeks family,1995

The consultants' football
team, 1998

Cutting the first sod with a glass of champagne for the new Elmstead Unit, 1998. The hospital was not "dry" then!

Tom Harris
(Consultant ENT surgeon) and the staff of the world-renowned Voice Clinic, 1998

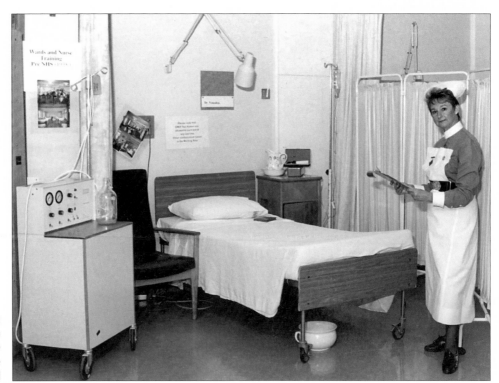

Hospital Open Day 1998;
Sister Brown poses in
1950s uniform with the
ward furniture of the
period

The hospital's general
managers, 1999
Back row (left to right):
Robin Sanham, Linda
Stimpson, Colin Cary
Front row: Karen Deacon,
Virginia Joy, Julia Millard

Michael Gotlieb
(Consultant radiologist)
receives the keys for the
Sidcup MRI Unit from
manager Lesley Harmes,
1999

2000 to the present

It's very difficult to tell tales of the present. So here are some photographs!

Left
S/N Shirley Patel starts the demolition of the old residences, 2000

Right
The Frognal medical Prize is presented to Dr Kendal by the Clinical Tutor, Dr Kevin Kelleher

Patricia Hodge MP helps the Millennium Volunteers plant a tree in the Women's Wing garden, 2000

Then

and now:

The Chapel,
1948 and 2004

In gentle silence of the Chapel here
One feels, indeed, God must be near;
The reverence and the sense of peace
From earthly problems give release –
If only for that passing hour
One spends within this peaceful bower.

The opening of the new Frognal Centre Library, 2000: Howard Stoate MP (GP Tutor) with Sir Edward Heath

As chairman, I have been privileged to meet many notable and important visitors. However the visitor who stands head and shoulders above many is Sir Edward Heath, a loyal friend to Queen Mary's for many years. A memory I shall always treasure is of escorting him on his annual broadcast on our hospital radio. These broadcasts are outstanding. The doyen of Queen Mary's radio, Pet, asks ferocious questions – making Jeremy Paxman look like a pussy cat.

On this particular occasion Pet generously let me ask a question, an opportunity I seized, asking his views on the Euro. We were then treated to 15 minutes of detailed economic theory. Wise and considered, but probably not what our listeners expected when they tuned in! As we came off air, Sir Edward chuckled in his unique way (made famous by Mike Yarwood) and said "You have no idea how much an American university would have paid me for that".

Elizabeth Butler

Left
Emma Noble with a cheque from local school children for the Acorn Appeal, 2000; in the back ground the Mayor and Mayoress of Bexley and John Austin MP

Right
Dr Saad Rassam (Consultant haematologist) is presented with a cheque by patient Ted Alger, 2000

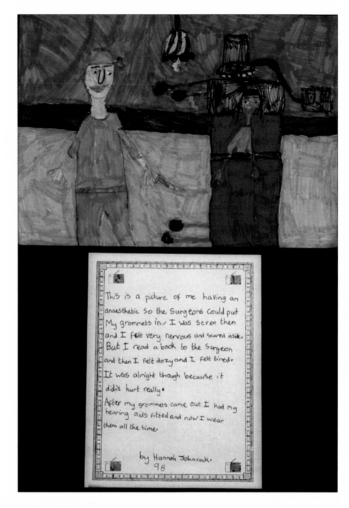

Science Week 2000;
a painting by Hannah
Johncock depicting her
anaesthetic

The post room staff,
Keith Preece and
Roger Kirby, 2002

A special award for service presented by the London Borough of Bexley to Steve Rovai (left), who has raised substantial sums of money for the hospital through raffles and discos, with Lynn Lewis, Iris Presswell and David Nowell (an Elmstead Unit client), 2003

Another "backroom boy"; Bill David, hospital photographer, who took many of the modern pictures in this book

Staff can be nominated for two monthly awards – Team and Employee of the Month – and are rewarded with a certificate and gift. Many hospital staff are unsung heroes, and the awards offer the opportunity for them to be recognised for their hard work and dedication.

Staff of the Newland Unit, Team of the Month January 2000

Charlton Athletic players on a Christmas visit to the children's ward, December 2002

The portering staff, Team of the Month February 2002

Outpatient reception staff, team of the Month May 2003

Employee of the Month January 2004: Stuart Rickman, Occupational Therapy Technical Officer with the Chief Executive Helen Moffatt and Human resources Director Mike Sillitoe

The retirement of
Val Greenwood,
Postgraduate Centre
Manager, 2003, with
Clinical Tutors past and
present.
Left to right:
Peter Savage,
Andrew Bamji.
Mrs Greenwood, William
Barry and Kevin Kelleher

The new hospital Day
Nursery, 2004

Chief Executive
Helen Moffatt,
Chairman Liz Butler, the
deputy Mayor of Bexley
and John Austin MP with
Lady Wallace and her son
at the opening of the
Wallace Garden, 2004

The cake made for the 75th anniversary commemoration service, November 2004

Look along the ward out there
The patients needing love and care,
So different each in many a way
A changing ward most every day.
For washing, comfort, general care,
For pills and potions, combing hair,
Good clean beds, for food and drink,
For all these things we are the link
That doctors and the patients need
Our every act, our every deed
To bring each patient back to health
Which is their riches and their wealth.
These are our jobs, this is the way
That nurses care most every day.

Composed by David Hammond
while an inpatient of Queen Mary's Hospital,
and read by him at the
anniversary service, November 2004.

The George Wallace garden outside the Oak Tree Restaurant, 2004

The Trust Board, November 2004
Front row (L to R)
Sarah Dawson, (Chief Nurse), Helen Moffatt, Elizabeth Butler (Chairman), Heather Nunnerley (Non-Executive Director), Deborah Tarrant (Human Resources Director.
Back row:
Colin Allies, Donna Bryant (Non-Executive Directors), Liz Roberts (Medical Director), Simon Perks (Operations Director),

Then

Now

The front entrance in 1929 and 2004

Memories take time to collect. Looking to the future we expect that many of today's staff and patients will, in years to come, have some recollections that might be worth sharing. If you have been entertained by this small booklet perhaps you would like to contribute to the next one in 2014. We always welcome any stories, photographs or other memorabilia from any era; send to

Dr Andrew Bamji FRCP
Curator, Gillies Archives
Queen Mary's Hospital, Sidcup, Kent DA14 6LT

You can also see some of the hospital's Archive collection on the Internet at
http://website.lineone.net/~andrewbamji/index.htm